the
CULTURED
Cabbage

the
CULTURED
Cabbage

Rediscovering the Art of Making Sauerkraut

Klaus Kaufmann ∾ Annelies Schöneck

Published by *alive* books
PO Box 80055, Burnaby BC Canada V5H 3X1
Copyright © 1997 by Klaus Kaufmann and Annelies Schöneck

Cover Photo: Siegfried Gursche
Inside Photos: Siegfried Gursche
Food Stylist: Stephen Case
Typesetting/Layout: Corina Messerschmidt
Cover Design: Corina Messerschmidt
Illustrations: Corina Messerschmidt

First edition - March 1998

Canadian Cataloguing in Publication Data
Kaufmann, Klaus 1942–

The cultured cabbage

Previous ed., by Annelies Schöneck, has title: Making sauerkraut and pickled vegetables at home.
Includes bibliographical references and index.
ISBN 0-920470-66-1

1. Sauerkraut. 2. Pickled foods. 3. Vegetables--Preservation. 4. Cookery (Sauerkraut). I. Schöneck, Annelies. II. Title. III. Schöneck, Annelies. Making sauerkraut and pickled vegetables at home.
TP444.S27S2313 1998   641.4'6   C98-910096-0

The recipe for Sauerkraut Onion Biscuits (© 1994 Carla Emery) is excerpted and adapted with permission of the publisher from *The Encyclopedia of Country Living* by Carla Emery. Published by Sasquatch Books, Seattle (800) 775-0817.

Printed and bound in Canada on acid-free paper

To Sylvia Reinhard, PhD, a good friend
and a professional biochemist and cancer researcher.
In the summer of 1975, during Christmas in the Kalahari
Desert, Sylvia convinced me that an approach involving
the whole organism is essential in the treatment
and prevention of cancer.
We both hold that fostering a proper mindset and eating
the right foods are the cornerstones and bedrock
of the fight against cancer.

—Klaus Kaufmann

Contents

Part II Vegetables in Ferment

Part III Healing With Lactic Acid Fermentation

Acknowledgments

This book would not have been possible without the good will and good advice of our many co-workers, in particular, our publisher, Siegfried Gursche, and our editors, especially Kathy Zia. While Klaus added the more technical and scientific "stuff" to this work, the main credit remains with Annelies, who is the sole author of the original *Making Sauerkraut and Pickled Vegetables at Home*, on which this present work is based. A special thank you is also due to Baz Edmeades, who translated Annelies's original work into English. This book owes its great looks, pictures, photography and all the artwork in general to the professional staff in *alive*'s art-room. And finally, we acknowledge the unrecognized pioneers in the art of sauerkraut making, as well as those who continue the tradition of fermenting this delicious food from scratch. May sauerkraut be the blessed vegetable of choice on every plate at least once a week.

There is a great treasure of abundance of blessings hidden in "kraut" and buried in rock. Sweet, holy nature, let me walk in your path.[1]

To Nature
Graf von Stolberg, 1775

Introduction

The growing health and natural lifestyle movement is taking great strides toward rediscovering the simple remedies and healing agents that reside plentifully in fresh and raw fruits and vegetables. Yet, at the same time, an opposing and seemingly greater force is pushing more and more consumers in the direction of frozen and processed foods, which have tripled their sales in Canada and the United States over the past year (1996). The public, in its continuous search for convenience meals, seems to be turning away from fresh, raw and healthful foods to frozen and canned goods. No wonder the medical industry is booming.

There is, however, a growing awareness of the value of simple traditional foods for their wonderful taste and health-enhancing properties. An increasing number of people are realizing that the basis of good health is good nutrition; thus, many people are achieving better health simply by improving their eating habits. It seems that everything else follows.

The first step to improving your diet is to recognize its shortcomings. This is not always easy. The ill effects of the "typical" North American diet are slow to accumulate and often stay hidden for many years. A high protein intake tends to mask a lack of vitamins, enzymes, minerals and trace elements caused by eating nutrient-deficient vegetables.

It may take a while for the toxic by-products produced as a result of metabolizing excess protein to create serious problems. What sometimes develops instead of outright illness is a kind of a twilight condition between health and sickness in which we are "well fed, but badly nourished."
The aim of this book is to help those who want to be well nourished. The secret of good nourishment comes mainly from our plant world. Yet fresh vegetables are not always in season and so we must look for means of preserving them for use throughout the year. It so happens that there is a method of doing just that—one that has the added benefits of bestowing superior taste and valuable healing properties to the vegetables so treated. This method of preservation is through lactic acid fermentation.

"Why," you might ask, "should I start preserving my vegetables by fermentation instead of freezing them?" As you will soon learn, lactic acid-fermented vegetables are both great tasting and a component of natural healing. It is time to reacquaint ourselves with the centuries-old technology of lactic acid fermentation. Its methods are simple, but nonetheless they require care and attention for successful results. Getting used to healthier food in itself helps us to strengthen our natural instincts for nutritious eating. Our bodies will learn to recognize what they need. As Paracelsus said, "Simplicity is the key."

A quarter of the meat that most people eat is quite enough for good health. The rest makes people ail, makes their money purse fail and to physicians gives wealth.[2]

Old Egyptian Wisdom

Part I
All About Kraut

Sour Power

In case you had any doubts, sauerkraut is not about
Germans, though one of us, Klaus, is proud to be a Kraut.
Sauerkraut is merely a southern German and Austrian word
for cabbage. Now "sauer" in English means "sour"; thus,
sauerkraut is sour cabbage.

There are very special things about sour cabbage and
other lactic acid-fermented vegetables that we will discover
together—like their great taste, how to prepare them, how to
use them in mouth-watering recipes and, most importantly,
why they make us and keep us healthy, rejuvenated and
vitally connected to Mother Earth.

Lactic acid fementation allows us to eat fresh, locally-
grown vegetables even in the middle of winter. What is
more, it is low in calories, provides good roughage and is
easily digested—even by people suffering from diabetes and
lactose problems. Finally, it can be easily made at home once
we have let Mother Earth do her thing.

From Cultivation to Preservation

As consumers, we should be more aware of the all-impor-
tant connection between fertilization and the cultivation of
our food plants. Food production is quite different from all
other forms of production; you can't ensure high quality by
simply selecting what looks to be a good final product.

You have to start by ensuring, as far as possible, that the right methods of cultivation have been used. The nutrients in our agricultural lands have been exhausted by overfarming and by the use of artificial fertilizers. The soil has been made sterile by chemical herbicides and insecticides and we are left with farmlands that can only produce feeble plants that don't keep well at all. Only today are we returning to organic farming, tellingly learning the ways of our ancestors.

When shopping for vegetables, we tend to choose according to size and shape, whereas scent, flavor, natural sweetness and the intensity of the color actually tell us far more about the quality of the product. Healthy soil, complete with the requisite nutrients, produces healthy plants that contain many of the substances necessary for our health. Our well-being therefore, is being passed up to us all the way from healthy microorganisms in the soil. It is no exaggeration, then, to say that "health is contagious," and that it starts with the humblest elements in the soil.

The aim of food preservation should not strictly be to prevent food from decay. The process of preservation should also improve and refine the food quality so that fragrance and aroma are added and digestibility is improved. Lactic acid fermentation—the form of preservation we are exploring in this book—does all these things. Lactic acid fermenta-

Healthy soil, complete with the requisite nutrients, produces healthy plants.

tion has played an important role in the history of mankind because of its health-giving and preservative qualities. Archeological finds have shown that even during the hunter-gatherer stage of our development, people fermented a plant similar to cabbage.

History and Tradition

The first written instructions on lactic acid fermentation are found in the writings of the Roman scholar Pliny in 50 AD. The Romans greatly appreciated sauerkraut and other lactic acid-fermented products. On extended journeys to the Middle East, Emperor Tiberius carried several barrels of sauerkraut as protection against intestinal infections. In medieval Europe, lactic acid-fermented foods were an essential part of the daily meal.

But even before that, cabbages were cultivated in ancient Egypt and Greece. In the second century BC, the Greek philosopher Theophrastus mentioned three types of cabbage in his writings on plants. Dioscurides, a Greek physician, wrote of cabbage, "it is healthier if only warmed than cooked." In 200 BC, Cato the Elder praised cabbage as "the very best vegetable." And, as with so many things, the Germans maintained this practice and later adopted the Slavic method of using lactic acid fermentation. With the disappearance of monasteries, this knowledge, too, was forgotten, only to be rediscovered twice. Once by Captain Cook, and once by us!

Attention was focused anew on the dietetic importance of sauerkraut when, in the eighteenth century, Captain Cook sailed around the world without losing a single man to scurvy during his famous three-year voyage. Because sauerkraut contains vitamin C, it, together with the lime juice carried aboard the *Endeavour*, helped to eliminate scurvy and allowed crews to stay on board for protracted periods without suffering deficiency diseases or malnutrition. Thus did a new era in navigation begin with the introduction of sauerkraut into the seafaring diet.

Traditional lactic acid fermentation is of great importance in South East Asia, where it is used to preserve fish, fruits and vegetables. There, the technique of preservation is crucial because food spoils rapidly in the warm, moist climate. China and Japan can also boast of age-old methods of lactic acid fermentation. Miso, a product that the Japanese ferment from soybeans, rice and barley, and which has become very popular in the West, is only one example of this art. The preparation of this product is an annual ritual during which the otherwise hard-to-digest soy protein is refined into a valuable nutritional supplement.

The Chinese have been fermenting cabbage for thousands of years, and prescribe sauerkraut juice for various physical ailments. One story has it that lactic acid fermentation was discovered accidentally during the building of the Great Wall of China: the poor workers building the wall owned no individual dishes, so all foods were dumped into one crock. After a few days, the flavor started changing....

Attention was focused anew on the dietetic importance of sauerkraut when, in the eighteenth century, Captain Cook sailed around the world without losing a single man to scurvy — a feat made possible by the prominence of sauerkraut in the sailors' diet.

CAPTAIN COOK'S "ENDEAVOUR"

The people of India make a cabbage paste out of sauerkraut juice. And eating in Russia and the Balkans is unthinkable without lactic acid-fermented products. There, people have long enjoyed kefir[4] and yogurt as well as a fermented product so common that we all take it for granted: sourdough bread. The Russian national dish, "kapusta," is a mixture of white cabbage, tomatoes, carrots, apples, pears, cucumbers and lots of herbs. Borscht, the traditional Russian soup, is made with lactic acid-fermented beets.

Another important group of lactic acid-fermented products includes fermented drinks like sour milk, kefir, buttermilk and yogurt. These drinks have played an important role in the history of human nourishment. They were found in different forms in every ancient culture. People realized very early on that lactic acid counteracts putrefaction and other disease-causing processes.

In Russia and Poland, the original lactic acid-fermented drink is still common today under the name "kvass," which is derived from a Slavonic word meaning "acid." Kvass doesn't refer to any particular drink, it is really a collective name for a whole group of lactic acid-fermented beverages, made according to a number of recipes[5]. Apples, pears, berries and root plants are mixed together in various proportions. Flour (or malted barley or rye) is then added and mixed with different herbs, peppermint being the most popular. By adding sauerkraut (or its juice) to this mixture lactic acid bacteria is produced.

The stimulating and healing effects of lactic acid-fermented vegetables:

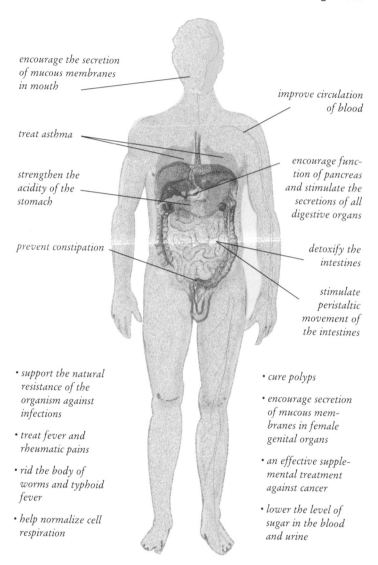

encourage the secretion of mucous membranes in mouth

improve circulation of blood

treat asthma

strengthen the acidity of the stomach

encourage function of pancreas and stimulate the secretions of all digestive organs

prevent constipation

detoxify the intestines

stimulate peristaltic movement of the intestines

• *support the natural resistance of the organism against infections*

• *treat fever and rheumatic pains*

• *rid the body of worms and typhoid fever*

• *help normalize cell respiration*

• *cure polyps*

• *encourage secretion of mucous membranes in female genital organs*

• *an effective supplemental treatment against cancer*

• *lower the level of sugar in the blood and urine*

Lactic Acid Bacteria

Lactic acid is formed as a product of energy exchange during the metabolism of microorganisms and other life forms, including plants, animals and man. The name stems from the fact that this product was first isolated in sour milk. The salts of lactic acid are thus known as "lactates." (The word also carries the meaning of "secretes milk.") Lactic acid bacteria cause catabolic changes to certain sugars that are present in their environment. The changes result in two new products: lactic acid and carbon dioxide. The lactic acid causes a curdling (of milk protein, for example), and therefore becomes more easily digestible. The lactic acid process brings about another boon: a natural preservation of the fermented food. There are, in fact, two kinds of lactic acid bacteria: one that is adapted to milk and milk products, and one that is adapted to plants.

Bacterial flora are responsible for providing lactic acid to the mucous membranes in the mouth, the intestines and the female genital organs. In the plant kingdom, species growing close to the soil have the most lactic acid bacteria. It is important to note that almost all vegetables are plentifully supplied by nature with lactic acid-forming bacteria. Traditional methods of lactic acid fermentation preservation (that do not involve the addition of a "starting" bacterial culture) rely strongly on this fact. Vegetables come equipped with their own lactic acid bacteria, and starting cultures are only necessary with milk products, salami and other kinds of sausage, as well as some fish preserves.

Lactic acid bacteria prevent decay not only in food products but in the bowels as well. Acetylcholine, which is produced during fermentation, stimulates the peristaltic movement of the intestines. It assists the circulation of the blood and prevents constipation by promoting bowel movements. Lactic acid-fermented products have a harmonizing effect on the stomach: they strengthen the acidity of the gastric juice when hydrochloric acid production lags, and lessen it when production is up. Lactic acid acts like a key that fits neatly into the secretion glands of the stomach—to lock and unlock those glands in accordance with the varying needs of the organism. Within the organism, lactic acid maintains the balance between acids and alkalis. Its rich vitamin C content supports the natural resistance of the organism against infections. Lactic acid encourages the function of the pancreas, which in turn stimulates the secretions of all the digestive organs. Of special importance to people with diabetes is the fact that the carbohydrates in lactic acid-fermented foods have already been broken down and do not, therefore, make heavy demands on the pancreas.

Lactic acid-fermented products are excellent for an enfeebled digestive system, which is caused by eating weak foods, exposure to polluted air and environmental diseases. It compensates for nutritional sins of both omission and commission. Lactic acid-fermented food is also a useful addition to the diet of cancer patients, where it serves as an effective supplemental treatment. World-renowned physician Dr. M.O. Bruker recommends daily intake of lactic acid-fermented vegetables or fermented milk products for detoxification and as a remedy against cancer. "Much doesn't help much" is an old saying that holds true for the use of lactic acid-fermented vegetables. The positive effect of lactic acid-fermented products lies in their regular use, not in consuming vast quantities sporadically. Accordingly, consuming three to four tablespoonfuls of sauerkraut daily, preferably raw (uncooked), can be sufficient to ward off disease, constipation and other intestinal problems.

A century ago Father Kneipp, the German "father of natural healers," had this to say about sauerkraut: "It is truly a broom for stomach and intestines. It takes away the bad juices and gases, strengthens the nerves and stimulates blood formation. You should eat it even if other cabbage is forbidden in your diet. Eat it moderately, well chewed, and do not drink anything with it."

New books and articles about sauerkraut are continually appearing, with descriptions of new discoveries and confirmation of its therapeutic effect. A great deal of research is now being done on lactic acid and its positive influence on our bodies.

Basic Information for the First-Time Pickler

The Fermentation Crock

The idea of having a special crock for fermentation is an ancient one. In China and Korea such containers have been used for thousands of years.

There are, of course, a variety of containers you can use to pickle vegetables, and as we will see, each has its own advantages and disadvantages. With the traditional kind of fermentation crock (which is still used in parts of Europe), keeping the fermenting vegetables free of kahm yeast can be a real problem. Kahm, a pasty, white substance, forms on top of the contents where there is access to fresh air. It isn't in the least harmful but because it gives the cabbage a bad taste it must be regularly removed. Every fourteen days, therefore, the cloth, board and stone that cover the vegetables in the traditional fermentation crock have to be washed or even boiled. This continuous problem is no doubt one of the reasons why people turned away from lactic acid fermentation to other preservation methods.

The good news is that a new fermentation crock manufactured by Harsch, a German company, has a patented gutter and lid that does away with the need for the constant cleaning. Kept in a cool place, this new crock can be left alone for months while the vegetables inside get better and better. The only chore that the new crock demands is that you occasionally top up the water in the gutter that seals off the contents from the outside air.

Not only the design, but the materials and process used in the manufacture of this stoneware crock are new. Covered with a lead-free glaze, it doesn't easily pick up the flavors of the various vegetables that ferment in it, and it is very easy to clean. The thick sides of this crock make it quite heavy, but its life expectancy is almost limitless. Instead of the weak handle of the traditional pots that tended to break easily, the Harsch crock features sturdy carrying handles that cannot break. In addition to serving as handles, they add to the stability of the gutter by acting as buttresses.

The crock comes with two small, semicircular stoneware "weight stones" that are designed to rest on top of the vegetables to create the pressure necessary for fermentation, and to protect the food from decay. Like the crock itself, the weight stones will not take on the aroma or flavors of the fermenting vegetables.

With the Harsch crock there is no need for the traditional paraphernalia of cloth, board or stone—and the kahm yeast no longer forms. During fermentation, carbonic acid forms and the water-filled gutter keeps this carbonic acid in the crock where it prevents the formation of kahm yeast. Excess carbon dioxide can, however, escape through the water seal. A happy little "gloop-gloop" noise will let you know when this is happening.

While the carbonic acid can escape from the crock, no outside air can get in. The carbonic acid layer that accumulates in the crock combines with free oxygen and water. This process creates a vacuum, or low-pressure environment, that should not be disturbed. At this time, therefore, you should do nothing but refill the gutter when necessary.

Take care to allow space for the accumulating carbonic acid by leaving at least an inch (2.5 cm) of free space at the top. There should be at least an inch of fluid or brine covering the weight stones. If the fluid level drops below the stones, top it up with boiled salted water (use a ratio of one tablespoon of salt to one quart or liter of water). After emptying, it is easy to clean the glazed fermentation crock as well as the lid and the weight stones. All the different parts must be cleaned thoroughly to prevent mold build-up.

Do not be startled if suddenly all the water seems to disappear from the gutter; just move the lid slightly (don't lift it!) and you will notice that the water is still there—the vacuum has merely drawn it upward inside the lid.

Preserving Jars

You can use ordinary glass preserving jars for fermentation if you wish, or any glass jar with a twist lid. The essential thing is that the lids close tightly. Check the lids of used vacuum jars carefully as they may have been damaged when the

jar was opened. You might have to use double rubber rings to get a good, tight seal if you are using preserving jars. Prepare the food in the same way as you would if you were using a fermentation crock. You can then press the vegetables into the jar making sure you don't fill it to more than eighty percent of its capacity.

When preserving in jars there should always be one-half inch (1 cm) of brine on top of all fermenting vegetables as some liquid will escape the jar as vapor. For the same reason the sealed jars must be stored on a towel for any escaping liquid will dribble down the sides.

The jars must be kept in the dark during the fermentation stage and subsequent storage. Put them in a carton, or cover them with a cloth. Using smaller containers like twist-top jars allows you to preserve smaller batches of vegetables, and it also makes it more practical for small families and single people to benefit from lactic acid fermentation. It is, however, easier to obtain good results when working with larger amounts of vegetables at any one time because a larger number of microorganisms will then be interacting with each other. Plastic jars are not recommended as harmful substances can leech into preserved foods over time.

Open Stoneware Pots

You may prefer to use the traditional open stoneware pot pictured below. When working with these stoneware pots, fill about seventy-five percent of the pot with crushed vegetables and cover them with a clean linen cloth. Then put a weight stone on top of the cloth. A water- and acid-proof stone such as granite must be used—limestone or marble will dis-

solve in the carbonic acid. If you do not have a suitable stone, put a plate or board on top that covers the vegetables as much as possible. Birch or beech are the woods traditionally used for this purpose. Don't use fir or pine. Their strong odors could easily be transferred to the vegetables. Cloth, stone and board have to be sterilized in boiling water before use. The open pots have to be tended very carefully. Remember that the white yeast or kahm must be removed every ten to fourteen days, the stone and board must be cleaned, and the cloth washed or boiled. Fasten a plastic bag over the pot to protect the contents from air.

Choosing Your Vegetables

If you are a gardener, you get to choose when your vegetables are harvested. There are, however, some minor rules to obey. For instance, don't harvest vegetables destined for preservation directly after a rainy period. Wait a day or

two. Lactic acid bacteria are present on most plants as surface culture, and their numbers diminish during rainy weather. If you're the gardener you can also avoid the use of pesticides or artificial fertilizers, which will wreak havoc with the original flora. Hopefully, your soil will be rich in nutrients. Lactic acid bacteria are very demanding about their nourishment; they need fermentable sugar, minerals, trace elements and almost all the B vitamins for their development.

The following vegetables are suitable for fermentation:

beans	beets
cabbage (white, red, Savoy)	cauliflower
celery	cucumbers
kohlrabi	leeks
onions	peppers
radishes	rutabaga
tomatoes	turnips

Clean the vegetables well, making sure they are free of soil. An interesting way of preserving, and one that is still common in Romania and Bulgaria, is to leave the vegetables whole. You will find a recipe for this in Part II. We have always had good results with preserving whole vegetables. How long will lactic acid-fermented vegetables last? In a cool, dark basement, you can keep them for a year or more.

Herbs and Spices

It is hard to think of preserving vegetables without using herbs. Can you imagine a pickle without the dill? Sauerkraut without juniper berries and caraway seeds is equally unthinkable.

Herbs are not just used for their wonderful flavors. They are also rich in minerals and trace elements—the very substances that are all too often lacking in our diets. Herbs have another function that is particularly important in preservation: many of them have the ability to prevent decay. Juniper, garlic and horseradish, to mention but a few, have been used for this purpose since time immemorial, though they are generally more famous for the flavors they impart.

The following herbs, spices and vegetables are frequently used to enhance flavor in lactic acid fermentation:

bay leaves	caraway seeds
cloves	coriander
dill	garlic
horseradish	juniper berries
onions	pimentos
raspberry leaves	savory
tarragon	tomatoes
yellow mustard seeds	

Lactic acid fermentation allows the garlic lover to indulge his or her fancy without jeopardizing social graces. Garlic tastes almost nutty after fermentation, and its "hot" quality adds a very special flavor to vegetables.

Don't hold back on the onions when you preserve. They are good for you and for the fermentation process.

Lactic acid-fermented onions are also more easily digestible, even for people who cannot eat them raw or boiled. Lactic acid fermentation rehabilitates the aggressive onion in a most effective way, converting it into a mild and pleasant vegetable.

Onions, either whole or cut into a few big chunks, are put directly into the fermentation container and covered with liquid. Be careful though, they can lose their delicious etheric oils very easily if you cut them open and then leave them lying on the kitchen counter.

Coriander is related to dill and caraway and belongs to the "umbelliferous" family, which includes parsley and carrots. Freshly chopped, it has a wonderful aroma—like a mixture of caraway, aniseed and lemon. Use it uncut for preserving.

Go easy on the pimento and the cloves! You don't want more than a hint of their presence in the preserve, as they can be quite obtrusive in larger amounts. If you still have dill, tarragon and savory by the time fall comes around, cut and dry them. They will be useful later on for the preservation of root vegetables.

Tomatoes, while not herbs, are a valuable supplement in preserves as nourishment for the lactic acid bacteria. Fresh raspberry leaves, as well as black currant leaves, are rich in lactic acid bacteria and also add a delicious flavor to preserves.

Utensils

No matter what containers you use, it is imperative that they are squeaky clean. Use hot water on the pots and avoid strong detergents. Let the pots dry in the open air or in the sun, if possible. Shredding is often necessary in lactic acid-fermented preserves. Crushing is a good alternative, and you will sometimes want to do both. Use your discretion.

If you expect to be preparing large quantities of vegetables for lactic acid fermentation, invest in a large wooden crusher or potato masher for pressing the vegetables tightly into the jars, and a whetstone to sharpen your knives for shredding. Sharpen each knife's edge first, as if you were cutting slices off the whetstone, keeping the blade at a constant angle. Most smooth, flattened river stones will work just as well as a store-bought whetstone.

Water

Unlike spring water, tap water containing chlorine must be boiled. As we've mentioned, you have to add salt to any water you put into the crock after fermentation has started. Always boil this water, and add the salt while the water is still hot, making sure the salt completely dissolves.

Salt

Because many of us are trying to reduce the salt in our diets, it's natural that we should question the role of salt in lactic acid fermentation. Vegetables contain proteins in addition to carbohydrates, and proteins tend to putrefy when they break down. Salt is used to prevent this from happening, and is especially important in the early stages before the lactic acid has accumulated in sufficient quantities to have a preservative effect. Experience has shown that adding salt that weighs between 0.8 and 1.5 percent of the total weight of the vegetables will result in a product that is both tasty and long-lived. The following will make it easier to add the right amount of salt:

- 2 tsp salt to 1 lb (454 g) cabbage
- 7 tbsp salt to 17 1/2 lbs (8 kg) cabbage
- 3 tbsp salt to 5 quarts cabbage
- (45 ml salt to 5 liters cabbage)

If there is not enough salt, the yeast takes over and we get alcohol fermentation, which brings about decay. If this is your first try at fermenting vegetables, stick to the recommended amount of salt until you are more experienced. Use of the fermentation crock will minimize the need for salt.

Use only pickling salt or sea salt. Sea salt is excellent for lactic acid fermentation because it contains many minerals and trace elements. Vegetables grown organically require less salt because of their superior quality. And cabbage is the only vegetable that can be fermented with very little salt or no salt at all—most likely because its leaves are particularly rich in vitamins, minerals and naturally-occurring lactic acid.

Whey—A Fermentation Supplement

Line a strainer with a thin cloth and pour some warmed buttermilk or sour milk into it. The fluid that strains through is whey. Because it contains lactose and several vitamins and minerals, whey is an excellent aid to fermentation. It is essential to add whey to vegetables such as cucumbers, that don't have much nutritive substance.

A pint or one-half liter of sour milk yields one-half pint or one-quarter liter of whey. If you have access to fresh cows' milk and strain your whey from milk that has not been pasteurized, it has to be boiled before use. Don't throw away the curds left behind in the strainer as they are delicious by themselves or in any number of interesting recipes.

Pasteurization

Pasteurization is the process of heating foods such as milk and vegetables to kill any bacteria or microorganisms that could cause disease. In the case of pasteurized vegetables, however, this process also kills off the healthy lactic acid bacteria which aids digestion, fights disease and imparts superior flavors. Most commercially available sauerkraut is pasteurized merely to improve its shelf-life—but be under no illusions—the pasteurized product does not hold the same healing properties that the fermented product does.

Starting Cultures

We are often asked if there is a reliable starting culture that can be used to get the lactic acid fermentation process off to a good start. You can use juice from a previous lactic acid-fermented preserve, but this really doesn't guarantee success. As we have said, lactic acid fermentation is a dynamic process, and the bacterial composition of the finished product is very different from that found in the first stages of lactic acid fermentation. So, if you use high quality, fresh vegetables, add the right herbs, and follow instructions, you shouldn't have any problems getting the lactic acid fermentation process off to a fine start. Remember: organically grown vegetables come with their own "indigenous" lactic acid fermentation bacteria in their intracellular spaces and on their outside surfaces.

Do use a starting culture, though, if you wish. A lot of the best lactic acid fermentation information will come out of your own experience, and you might get good results from it.

Some vegetables, like cucumbers, produce plenty of juice during fermentation which can be used as a starting culture. Strain off this juice and store it in clean, dark bottles. There must be no air space left in the bottles. If you seal them properly, the contents will keep for ages. Disregard the white "shell" that may form over the contents: it is the same harmless kahm yeast that we spoke about earlier. This juice can be used as a starting culture, or as a dressing instead of vinegar, or as an aperitif before meals. Besides lactic acid, this juice contains minerals, vitamins and acetylcholine.

Storing Your Lactic Acid-Fermented Vegetables

It is important that you do not open the fermentation crock too often. Calculate your needs for two or three weeks, remove that quantity from the fermentation crock, transfer it into twist top jars and put them in the fridge. Open jars of lactic acid-fermented vegetables must be kept cool. If you wish, you can pour cold-pressed oil on top of the contents to minimize their exposure to air.

When you have used up two-thirds of the vegetables in the fermentation crock, transfer the remainder into smaller jars in order to free up the big one for further use.

...Cabbage is the physician of the poor.

Parisian physician Dr. Blanc (1881)

Part II
Vegetables in Ferment

Simplicity is the key.

Paracelseus

The Art of Successful Lactic Acid Fermentation

The basic requirements for lactic acid fermentation are:

- a certain concentration of salt
- a specific temperature
- an acid-free environment
- pressure on the foods being fermented

If these requirements are met, a process is started that is quite different from what would have happened if the foods had been left to themselves. A special kind of fermentation occurs during which lactic acid is formed. Microorganisms, yeast and bacteria all play a role in this process. These organisms can only develop, however, if suitable conditions prevail and if they receive enough nourishment. The art of successful lactic acid fermentation consists of creating these conditions; if one fails to create them the food doesn't ferment, it decays.

The process of lactic acid fermentation occurs in two different phases. First, there is a slight decomposition due to fermentation. The salt initially protects all vegetables from decay until enough lactic acid has formed. Eventually so much acid is produced that the bacteria that cause decay and the butyric acid (a fatty acid that inhibits the fermentation process) can no longer be produced. Yeast fungi, which contribute to the delicious and characteristic fermentation aroma, are also part of the initial fermentation process.

A successful first phase is the foundation on which the whole lactic acid fermentation process rests. It must take place quickly and must not be interrupted. In this first phase, temperature plays an important role. The ideal temperature for sauerkraut is 68–72°F (20–22°C) ; for cucumbers 64–68°F (18–20°C); and for carrots around 68°F (20°C).

After two days another phase begins: the lactic acid-producing bacteria start gaining the upper hand and eliminate all other bacteria. This process must not be rushed. Lower the temperature to 59–64°F (15–18°C) for cabbage and to about 18°C (64°F) for other vegetables. Fermentation should con-

1. Remove outer leaves from firm, mature heads of cabbage. Wash and drain. Remove core and shred with a knife or shredder.

2. Weigh 5 pounds carefully to ensure correct cabbage-salt proportions.

3. Measure 3 tablespoons pickling or sea salt and sprinkle over 5 pounds prepared cabbage. Mix well with spoon or hands. Allow 15–20 minutes for cabbage to wilt slightly.

4. Pack cabbage into a stoneware pot. Press firmly with a potato masher or hands until juice is drawn out to cover shredded cabbage.

5. Put a linen cloth on cabbage then lay a weight stone on top of the cloth, allowing no air to reach the cabbage. Ferment for approximately 5 to 6 weeks. Gas bubbles indicate that fermentation is occurring. Temperatures between 68° and 72° are ideal for fermentation.

6. Fasten a plastic bag over the pot to protect the contents from air. Remove any white yeast or kahm every ten to fourteen days.

tinue without any problem. Soon, it will reach the critical 4.1 pH-point, where butyric acid and decay bacteria can no longer form. It is during this phase that new substances like acetylcholine, vitamin C, vitamin B_{12} and enzymes are formed.

When fermentation stops—after ten to fourteen days (two to three weeks for cabbage)—the vegetables must be put in a cool place, ideally between 32–50°F (0–10°C). A thermometer set on top of the fermentation crock will show whether the temperature is right.

It is important not to open the fermentation crock before the end of fermentation; if you do, the carbon dioxide that prevents yeast formation will escape. Check occasionally to ensure that the water gutter is filled. If you use jars with twist lids, put them in a cool place for ten days without opening them. If you use open containers, the kahm layer must be removed in the way described in the section on open stoneware pots.

Once the vegetables have been put in a cool place, patience is required, as all biological processes need time. Acid formation only takes place during the first, or "warm," stage. (It is better, by the way, to make the warm period a little too long rather than too short.) Aroma develops during the cool "storage" period. To develop the aroma, bacteria need sugar and other nutrients. If all the sugar present has been used up during an overly long and warm fermentation, your product will be well preserved, but it will taste sour, so, stick to suggested fermentation times.

The lactic acid which has formed is an organic acid that does not acidify the body in the way that the digestion of meat, eggs and cheese does. It fits into the process of metabolism in a way that other fermented products like vinegar or alcohol simply do not. It links the breakdown and reconstruction in the organism in an astonishing way, and this is really the key to effective nutrition: we do not, after all, live by what we eat, but rather by what our bodies can digest and utilize.

We don't have to eat sauerkraut until we are overfull!
Small amounts, taken regularly, are quite sufficient to
initiate many healing processes.

Favorite Fermented Foods

White Cabbage

Throughout the history of human nutrition, white cabbage and its relatives have played an important role. The great American biochemist Ebert McCollum points out that the leaf of this plant is a complete foodstuff in itself. In fact, cabbage leaves have healing power, and the medicinal effects of cabbage are so vital that in 1881 Dr. Blanc, a Parisian physician, wrote, "cabbage could be in medical science what bread is in nutrition; cabbage is the physician of the poor."

Researcher Hans Rudolf Locher confirms that any form of cabbage has healing powers. He states that the juiciest, darkest and greenest leaves are the most effective for external applications in cases such as abscesses, bronchial asthma, bronchitis, pleurisy, gangrene, gout, bruises, contusions, crush injuries, and inflammations of the lymph nodes and the middle ear. In all of these conditions, the external and internal use of sauerkraut brings about healing.

Cabbage leaves can be applied externally in cases of soreness and inflammation. The leaves should be cut into strips and applied as a poultice that is renewed mornings and evenings. In acute conditions the leaves will turn brown within a few hours and must be replaced more often. When the leaves turn yellow and dry out, therapy can be considered concluded. The leaves can no longer find toxins to neutralize. (Unfortunately, this effect can also occur if the condition does not respond to cabbage leaf treatment.) External application must be supported by internal means as well, i.e., consuming sauerkraut and avoiding sugar and sugary foods, white flour, alcohol and nicotine.

Cabbage originated in Europe, where many varieties still exist. The synthesis of protein, carbohydrates and fats takes place in its leaves. The leaves' active cells that perform these tasks contain everything that is essential for our metabolism. Sauerkraut made from summer cabbage is ready for consumption after only fourteen days. It is delicious but not too durable. You should only ferment as much as you can eat within a fairly short time. For winter consumption, autumn cabbage is best. However, the essential point is to use only mature, sound cabbage, no matter when it ripened.

If you want to use little or no salt it is very important to start fermentation quickly. Warm up the container first, and heat the whey to 86°F (30°C). If you have never tried fermenting before, it's a good idea to start out with white cabbage. This vegetable is so rich in nutrients and lactic acid bacteria that it can normally be relied on to start and sustain its own lactic acid fermentation process with no trouble at all. It is, so to speak, ready-made for the job.

Simple Sauerkraut
(for a ten quart/liter fermentation pot)

17 1/2 lbs (8 kg) white cabbage
1 1/2 tbsp caraway seeds
7 tbsp pickling or sea salt

3 tbsp juniper berries
3–4 sour apples (optional)
1/4 quart/liter whey (optional)

Low-Salt Sauerkraut
(for a ten quart/liter fermentation pot)

17 1/2 lbs (8 kg) white cabbage
1 1/2 cups onions
1 1/2 tbsp caraway seeds

1 quart/liter whey
2 tbsp pickling or sea salt
20 juniper berries

Salt-Free Sauerkraut
(for a ten quart/liter fermentation pot)

17 1/2 lbs (8 kg) white cabbage
juice of 3 lemons

1 quart/liter whey
3 oz (80 g) glucose

The vitamin C content is highest in the green leaves, so don't imagine that the snow-white specimens are necessarily the best cabbages. Some of the outermost green leaves should, however, be removed. You can use them in soups or stews. Remember to save a few big leaves for the final layer. Clean the cabbage, cut out any bruised sections and the stalk—which should not be thrown away. It contains fermentable sugar and fine aromatic substances. Shred it on a coarse grater and mix it in with the cut and crushed leaves of the cabbage.

Mix all ingredients in a large bowl. Transfer this mix to the crock or preservation jar a bit at a time and pack the mix tightly. Repeat this process until the pot is about eighty percent full. Cover the last layer with a few large leaves. Do not exceed your eighty percent limit: fermentation will expand the cabbage, and you have to leave room for the weight stones. The water must cover the weight stones while still leaving a one inch (2.5 cm) air space at the top. Put the lid on the fermentation pot and fill up the gutter with water.

Put the pot in a warm place. The temperature should be between 68° and 72°F (20–22°C) for a few days. After fermentation has started, put the pot in a cool place for two to three weeks. In order for a slow fermentation to take place the temperature should be around 59°F (15°C).

Only after this time should you open the pot. You might have to rinse the stones and pour boiled, cooled salted water over the cabbage if it has dried. After that, put the pot in a cold place, ideally between 32° and 50°F (0–10°C). You can eat the sauerkraut after four weeks, but it will be even better if you leave it for a longer period.

Red Cabbage

Red cabbage can be preserved in the same way as white cabbage. Add apples, onions and bay leaves. Red cabbage, however, has to be mashed thoroughly as it is a very hard veg-

etable, and even heavy pressing might not extract enough juice. If that turns out to be the case, fill up the fermentation pot with a bit of whey, some lactic acid-fermented vegetable juice, or water.

Lactic Acid-Fermented Red Cabbage
(for a ten quart/liter fermentation pot)

17 1/2	lbs (8 kg) red cabbage	3–4	sour apples
1 1/2	cups onions	5–8	bay leaves
1/2	tsp caraway seeds	20	juniper berries

Preparation is the same as for white cabbage sauerkraut.

Savory Sauerkraut Soup
(serves two)

1/2	onion, finely diced	1/2	cup raw sauerkraut
1/2	cup Chardonnay wine	1	bay leaf
1/2	cup potatoes, diced	1	cup vegetable stock
1	clove	2	tbsp sour cream
1	tbsp fresh dill finely chopped		dash of savory
1	tsp unsalted, cultured butter (available in your grocer's freezer section)		dash of salt and pepper

Sauté onions in the butter. Add wine and all other ingredients except sour cream, salt and pepper. Cook for 45 minutes, adding water as necessary. Purée the soup with a hand mixer or blender. Return to the pot and bring to a boil again. Season with sour cream, pepper and salt. Refrigerate. Serve cold—your very own and unusual vichyssoise.

Making Sauerkraut
and
Pickled Vegetables at Home

Seven Simple Steps for Making Sauerkraut

Step 1
Grate cabbage into a large bowl.

Step 2
Add salt, herbs and spices.

Step 3
Mix together the cab
herbs and spices.

Step 4

Add berries where indicated.

Step 5

Using a potato masher, pack the cabbage mix tightly into the jar one layer at a time.

Steps 6–7

Place a cabbage leaf on top, add brine and seal the container.

Making Sauerkraut Using the Harsch Fermentation Crock

Pack the cabbage tightly into the crock using a potato masher or wooden crusher.

Be sure to leave one inch (2.5 cm) of free space at the top of the crock before putting the weight stones and lid in place.

At any time of year, sauerkraut makes a delicious entrée, appetizer or salad.

The Pickling Process

Step 1

Wash the vegetables thoroughly to remove any dirt or soil.

Step 2

Pack the vegetables, spices and herbs into the fermentation container. (This is an example of the Japanese Press which allows you to eat the lactic acid-fermented vegetables after only 2-4 weeks).

Step 3

If using a Japanese Press, put the lid in place and apply pressure to the vegetables.

Step 4

If you are pickling in jars you should store them on a cloth as water will escape through the seals and dribble down the sides.

Behold your pickled vegetables! Guten Appetit!

Kraut Pizza

(serves four)

pizza crust:

1 1/4	cups whole wheat flour	2	tbsp water
1/2	cup unsalted, cultured butter	1	bay leaf

Thoroughly mix flour, butter and salt with your hands until a fine texture is achieved. Work water into the mix in small portions. Do not knead. Let sit for two hours in the refrigerator before forming into crust.

topping:

1 1/2	cups raw sauerkraut		unsalted, cultured butter
1/4	cup eggplant, diced	3/4	cup Gruyère cheese, diced

Heavily salt the chopped eggplant and let it sit for 20–30 minutes. The salt will draw out excess water making the eggplant easier to sauté afterward. Using a paper towel, wipe away the excess salt. Sauté the eggplant in butter until soft. Add sauerkraut and stew slowly. Distribute the mixture evenly over the crust. Sprinkle cheese on top. Bake briefly in preheated oven at 475°F (250°C).

sauce:

2	tbsp whole wheat flour	2	eggs
1	cup kefir	1/2	cup yogurt
2	eggs	1	dash caraway seeds
1	dash salt		

Mix all ingredients. Pour over the prebaked pizza. Maintain same temperature and bake for another 25–30 minutes.

    Serve with a yogurt-seasoned butter lettuce. Delicious!

Tangy Teutonic Omelet

(serves two)

1/3	cup eggplant, diced	1/3	cup raw sauerkraut
1/2	tbsp cranberries	2	large free-range eggs
	dash sage		dash celery seed
	dash paprika		dash oregano
	dash black pepper	1/2	cup whipping cream,
1	tsp cranberries		whipped
	(for decoration)	1/4	cup Chardonnay
1	tsp unsalted, cultured		wine
	butter		

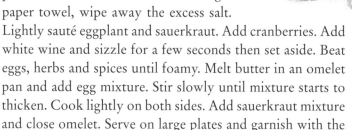

Heavily salt the chopped eggplant and let it sit for 20–30 minutes. The salt will draw out excess water making the eggplant easier to sauté afterward. Using a paper towel, wipe away the excess salt. Lightly sauté eggplant and sauerkraut. Add cranberries. Add white wine and sizzle for a few seconds then set aside. Beat eggs, herbs and spices until foamy. Melt butter in an omelet pan and add egg mixture. Stir slowly until mixture starts to thicken. Cook lightly on both sides. Add sauerkraut mixture and close omelet. Serve on large plates and garnish with the whipped cream and cranberries. Mouth-watering!

Sauerkraut Onion Biscuits

These hearty biscuits are made using your favorite bread recipe. Preheat your oven according to the temperature specified in your bread recipe. You can easily adapt this recipe by adding your favorite kraut spices or herbs to the sauerkraut mixture.

	enough bread dough for one large loaf
3	cups raw sauerkraut
1	onion, chopped

While the bread dough is in its
first rising, sauté the onion in a
small skillet until translucent.
Remove from heat and mix with
sauerkraut. When the dough
has risen, roll it out with a
rolling pin until it is 1/4 to 1/2
inch (1/2 to 1 cm) thick. Cut the dough into 8 inch squares
and put a heaping spoonful of the sauerkraut mixture in the
middle of each one. Pinch each square closed and let rise for
another half hour. Bake until golden brown and serve hot or
cold.

Sauerkraut with Apples

Pour cold-pressed oil onto the sauerkraut, and grate an
apple into the mix. Add chopped nuts if desired.

Sauerkraut with Onions

Mix sauerkraut with minced onions and cold-pressed oil.
Sprinkle with paprika before serving.

Try sauerkraut with celery, freshly grated carrots and
ground anise.

Cooked Sauerkraut
(serving suggestions)

Let's not forget cooked sauerkraut altogether. The following
recipe for two can be altered in many different ways by the
addition of sautéed onion, paprika, or pineapple. You will
notice that your lactic acid-fermented sauerkraut needs very
little cooking, and that it keeps its aroma, color and nutritional value.

Take two heaping cups of sauerkraut and divide into two
equal portions. Chop one of the portions finely and set
aside. In a medium-size pot combine the uncut sauerkraut, a

chopped apple (peeled), 1/2 cup of juniper berries and let cook over medium heat for 30 minutes. Usually the sauerkraut will not have enough juice so add water or apple juice as needed to prevent the mixture from drying out. If you want to bind the sauerkraut, grate a raw potato into it near the end of the cooking time and give it a few more minutes.

Just before serving, add chopped, uncooked sauerkraut (this gives the meal a piquant and fresh aroma and keeps it rich in vitamins) and drizzle in some cold-pressed oil. Serve with mashed potatoes and baked apples filled with raisins and nuts. An easily digested, delicious and nutritious meal!

Traditional German Rotkohl

In this recipe, rotkohl (red cabbage) is given a wintery flavor by combining cloves and bay leaves.

3–4	cups red cabbage sauerkraut	6	bay leaves
I	apple, peeled and chopped	10	cloves
2	medium onions, chopped		salt and pepper
I	tbsp cold-pressed oil		to taste

In a large skillet, sauté onions for two minutes then add sauerkraut, apple, bay leaves and cloves. Reduce heat and cover and let simmer for twenty minutes.

Cucumbers
Fresh, lactic acid-fermented cucumbers with their mild acidity and spicy taste are universal favorites. In ancient China, they were believed to encourage the qualities of imagination and inspiration.

Cucumbers grow rapidly during warm, humid summers. In conditions such as these, they also ferment rapidly. If, on the other hand, the summer has been cold and dry, it is important to add whey and a little more salt to prevent the cucumbers from turning soft. In Finland and Russia, during cool summers in which fermentation is slower, housewives put a few oak leaves into the fermentation container. The tannic acid of the oak helps to protect the cucumbers from decomposition until enough lactic acid has formed.

Lactic Acid-Fermented Cucumbers

Select medium-sized, hard cucumbers for fermentation. Clean and brush them to rid them of any dirt. Poke holes into them with a knitting needle or a sharp knife to facilitate the exchange of fluids. Larger cucumbers have to be cut into pieces.

Lactic Acid-Fermented Cucumbers

(for a one quart/liter preserving jar)

2 1/3	cups cucumbers	1	tsp mustard seeds
1	bay leaf		lots of fresh dill
2	tbsp whey	2	tbsp pickling or sea salt
1	clove garlic,	1	stem fresh tarragon
	finely chopped	1/8	tsp ground coriander
1/3	small tomato, whole		seeds
1	fresh horseradish root,	1/2	small onion, sliced in
	chopped (available in		rings or quartered
	Chinese markets)		

Pack the cucumbers, onion, garlic, tomato and herbs firmly into the preserving jar until the container is eighty percent full. Make a salt water solution by dissolving 2 tbsp of pickling or sea salt in 1 quart/liter of water. Fill the jar with salted water and whey making sure there is a 1/2 inch (1 cm) layer of liquid on top of the cucumbers. Leave the container at room temperature for ten days, then put it in a cold place. Cucumbers will be ready to eat after two to three weeks' cold storage.

Lactic acid-fermented cucumbers go well with bread and in salads. You can also make a sandwich spread or sauce from lactic acid-fermented cucumbers and onions. Simply mince the cucumbers and onions and add parsley and chives. Mix with some mustard and curds or sour cream.

Pumpkin and Squash

A few years ago, when calories were the be-all and end-all of "dieting," the fortunes of pumpkins went into decline. But now that we have begun to realize that excessive protein and refined foods also play a part in weight gain, and that proper nutrition is an important component in weight control, this traditional stand-by, with its marvelous cleansing and detoxifying qualities, is coming into its own once again.

Pumpkins chosen for lactic acid fermentation should not be too ripe or they will fall apart during fermentation. If they do fall apart, though, you needn't follow suit! Your lactic acid-fermented pumpkin will still be good tasting and nutritious, even if it is a little hard to handle.

As pumpkin lacks a strong taste of its own, you can add plenty of spices to make sure that the end product doesn't turn out too bland.

Lactic Acid-Fermented Pumpkin With Peppers

(for a one quart/liter preserving jar)

2	cups pumpkin or squash, peeled and cubed	1	tsp mustard seeds
1/3	cup green or red peppers, chopped	1/4	cup sour apples, chopped but unpeeled
4	tbsp onions	1/4	cup tomatoes
1/4	tsp cloves	1	clove garlic
4	tbsp whey or, if possible, lactic acid-fermented juice	2	bay leaves
			horseradish to taste
		1	tbsp pickling or sea salt

Lactic Acid-Fermented Pumpkin
With Lemons and Spice

(for a one quart/liter preserving jar)

2 1/2	cups pumpkin or squash	1/2	lemon, peeled and cubed
3/4	cup sour apples, chopped but unpeeled	1/2	cup quinces
1	inch (2 cm) piece fresh ginger root, chopped	1	tbsp cloves
		1/4	tsp cinnamon
3/4	cup whey, or lactic acid-fermented juice	1	tbsp pickling or sea salt

Prepare everything that you will need for preserving. Chop the peppers (which are used in the first recipe only), remove the seeds and white part, and cut the remainder into half-inch squares. If you want to do a really special job, boil the pumpkin peels and the pepper seeds for half an hour and use that water for filling up the preserving jar.

Pack layers of vegetables, herbs and salt very firmly into the jar. Mix whey or some lactic acid-fermented juice (these are optional) with the pumpkin/pepper seed extract (or tap water if you've decided to go the quick and convenient route, remembering to boil it if it is chlorinated) and pour this mixture over the vegetables. Pumpkin absorbs water so allow for this by adding a little less water to the jar.

Leave the sealed jar for eight to ten days at a temperature of 64–68°F (18–20°C), then put in cool storage.

Pumpkins can be tailored to suit a wide variety of tastes. Experiment to discover your own favorite flavor combinations!

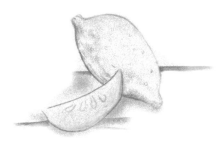

Pumpkin or Squash Salad Dressing

Lactic acid-fermented pumpkin can be used to supplement all kinds of dishes. It can be puréed in the blender and then used for salad dressings. Add some ground ginger, perhaps some freshly chopped herbs, and a bit of honey. Serve in small bowls as a dip.

Beans

Beans are the only vegetable that has to be cooked before preservation. They contain a toxic substance called phasin, a protein that interferes with digestion and decomposes when heated. Never serve raw beans on a salad plate!

Cut, wax and string beans, as well as broad or "tick" beans are suitable for lactic acid fermentation. The more tender they are, the better the end result will be. Be careful not to over-salt your beans.

Basic Lactic Acid-Fermented Beans

(for a one quart/liter preserving jar)

3 1/2 cups beans	1/2	small onion
savory to taste	3	tbsp pickling or sea salt
2 tbsp whey		

Lactic Acid-Fermented Beans
With Mustard and Dill

(for a one quart/liter preserving jar)

3 1/2	cups beans	2	tbsp whey
1	tsp yellow mustard seeds	1	tbsp horseradish
1	clove garlic		savory and dill
1	tbsp pickling or sea salt		blossoms to taste

Boil beans in lightly salted water (2 tbsp pickling or sea salt to 1 quart/liter of water) for five to ten minutes. For very tender beans, five minutes cooking time is enough. For larger amounts, cook one batch after the other in the same water.

Take care in all cases to avoid overcooking. Spread them on a cloth to cool. Next, layer the beans in the preserving jar together with the spices. Mix the whey with the water in which you boiled the beans, and pour this mixture so that there is 1/2 inch (1 cm) of liquid on top of the vegetables.

Leave the container at room temperature (64–68°F or 18–20°C), for eight to ten days, then put it in a cool place. After three weeks of storage the beans will be ready for consumption.

Cut Beans

Cut beans can be preserved raw or cooked, but it is better to play it safe and boil them before fermentation. Do not use hard beans. Remove those beans that have already formed seeds. Preparation is the same as in the other bean recipes.

Root Vegetables

Root vegetables, in addition to being well-suited to lactic acid fermentation, are potent antioxidants, vitamin-rich and full of fibers that control blood cholesterol levels. The orange-yellow colored vegetables such as carrots and yams are naturally sweet and are excellent sources of beta-carotene—a vitamin essential for the prevention of night-blindness. Root vegetables have the added bonus that they do not spoil quickly, but they do need to be cleaned thoroughly before use.

Basic Recipe for Lactic Acid-Fermented Root Vegetables

(carrots are used in this recipe for a one quart/liter preserving jar)

3 1/4 cups carrots, cleaned and cut

2 cups pumpkin or squash

1 garlic clove, chopped

1 clove

1 small piece of horseradish dried dill and tarragon to taste

2 tbsp lactic acid-fermented cucumber juice or sauerkraut juice (optional)

3 1/4 cups onions, peeled and cut

1 tsp mustard seeds

1 bay leaf

1 tsp yellow mustard seeds

1 tbsp pickling or sea salt

2 tbsp whey

Mix the carrots with salt, herbs and spices. Layer the spiced carrots tightly in the jar with the onions and garlic. Be careful not to mash the vegetables. In case the carrots do not produce enough of their own juice (which will most often be the case), add boiled salt water (2 tbsp of pickling or sea salt to 1 quart/liter of water) until they are just covered so the carrots will absorb more fluid. Leave the pot at room temperature (64–68°F or 18–20°C) for two to three days. Then store at a temperature of 64°F (18°C) for no longer than ten days. Finally store in a cool place. Root vegetables need at least four to six weeks of fermentation before they are ready to eat.

This root vegetable recipe is very flexible and lends itself to experimentation. You could try, for instance, substituting turnips for half of the carrots in the above recipe. Turnips will produce a mild acidity and impart a very appealing color.

Lactic Acid-Fermented Carrots and Onions

Mixed together, these vegetables make a simple, delicious salad. Onions can be cut in thin rings and eaten as snacks. They are easily digested and go well with all kinds of spreads. Also mix with endives or chicory.

Celery Root

Celery roots contain a whole bouquet of aromatic scents and are therefore well suited for mixing with milder kinds of vegetables. There is hardly a combination in which you will not appreciate its rich flavor. You will also get good results if you preserve celery roots by themselves as the main vegetable, along with only onions and herbs. Follow the basic recipe for root vegetables.

Radishes

The radish is by nature a winter preserve, and it tends to get a woody flavor during long storage. It has been used for both nutritional and medicinal purposes for centuries. It cleanses and detoxifies the system and acts as a diuretic.

Cleaning and cutting radishes can be a chore. For this reason, and the relatively strong odor of this vegetable, radishes aren't used as often as they might be in lactic acid fermentation. This is a pity because the same sulfuric oils that give it its strong, distinctive odor are extremely effective in inhibiting putrefaction. Lactic acid fermentation mellows the strong odors of these oils. All in all, this vegetable seems to be made for lactic acid fermentation. Radishes, onions and a few sour apples preserved together provide a delicious complement to almost any meal.

Lactic Acid-Fermented Radishes

(for a one quart/liter preserving jar)

2 1/2	cups cleaned, chopped radishes		1/4	cup sour apples, chopped
3/4	cup onions, coarsely chopped		1	tsp coriander seeds
1	tbsp pickling or sea salt		1	tsp caraway seeds
			2	tbsp whey

For preparation, see the basic recipe for lactic acid-fermented root vegetables.

Beets

Beets have been used for medicinal purposes for two thousand years. Their rich chemical and mineral composition gives them a wide range of medicinal functions and it has now been scientifically shown that the beet promotes cell respiration and stimulates the immune system. This promotes the recovery and normalization of tissues that have already begun to develop toward cancer.

Having said this, it is not all that easy to ferment beets. Your best bet is to preserve them together with white cabbage, onions and apples. If you do beets alone they will produce a thick, slimy juice that, although very aromatic and tasty, does not keep well. If you are going to preserve them alone, don't do too many of them at one time.

Lactic Acid-Fermented Beets

(for a one quart/liter preserving jar)

3 1/2	cups beets, chopped	horseradish to taste
1	tsp caraway seeds	some lactic acid-fermented
1/4	cup onions, coarsely chopped	juice (optional)
1	tbsp pickling or sea salt	boiled salt water for filling up the container (2 tbsp salt to 1 quart/liter water)
2	tbsp whey	
1	tsp mustard seeds	

Preparation is the same as in the basic recipe for lactic acid-fermented root vegetables.

Fill jar only three-quarters full as beets ferment heavily. The ideal fermenting temperature is around 64°F (18°C).

Lactic Acid-Fermented Beet Salad

(for a one quart/liter preserving jar)

2 1/3	cups beets, chopped		1	tsp mustard seeds
3/4	cup white cabbage, chopped		1/4	cup tangy apples, chopped
3/4	cup onions, coarsely chopped		1	bay leaf
1	tbsp pickling or sea salt some lactic acid fermented juice (optional)		1/4	quart/liter boiled water for filling up the
2	tbsp whey			container

Preparation is the same as in the basic recipe for lactic acid-fermented root vegetables. Fill the jar only three-quarters full as beets ferment heavily. The ideal fermenting temperature is around 64°F (18°C).

You can use beets for salads with apples and freshly ground caraway. Add horseradish mixed with sour cream.

Lactic acid-fermented beet is, of course, the basis of borscht, that proverbially cheap meal, and the national soup of Russia. Actually, traditional Russian borscht also contains beef and smoked bacon, but it is equally good the vegetarian way. Carefully cook a vegetable soup in accordance with the "whatever you happen to have" principle. Use carrots, cabbage, onions, leeks and herbs like celery leaves and savory.

If the soup is to be the main dish, add a few potatoes. Put the lactic acid-fermented beets into the finished soup for a wonderful flavor and an appealing red color. Spice with basil, and add sour cream to taste after serving.

Preserving Whole Vegetables

All vegetables can be preserved whole—all you need are big enough containers. In general, you will get a better result if you mix your vegetables rather than preserving one kind at a time. The reason for this is that the nutritional demands of the lactic acid bacteria are met particularly well by the broad spectrum of nutrients found in a variety of different vegetables.

Mura-Tura

This is a basic recipe you can adjust to your taste. All kinds of garden vegetables can be used: cucumbers, green tomatoes, ripe tomatoes, carrots, celery roots, small white cabbage heads, small cauliflower, beans (remember to cook them!), onions, peppers and corn.

(for a 10 quart/liter fermentation pot)

15	lbs (7 kg) vegetables	2	tbsp mustard seeds
2	tbsp coriander seeds		some dill
2-3	pieces of finger-length	1	cup pickling or
	horseradish root		sea salt
1/4	quart/liter whey		
	some lactic acid-fermented		
	fluid (optional)		

Clean all vegetables. If the beans have seeds, these must be shelled out. Poke holes in the cucumbers and tomatoes (green ones, too) to ensure that the lactic acid fermentation penetrates into their interiors. Cut peppers in half and remove the core. Small white cabbage heads or Savoy cabbage heads can be preserved either whole or in halves. Pack vegetables and herbs solidly into the fermentation container. Pour some whey and lactic acid-fermented fluid between the layers. Fill up with enough salted water to just about cover the vegetables. Place weight stones and lid on top and fill the water gutter. Keep the fermentation pot at 68°F (20°C) for two to three days, then move to a temperature of about 64°F (18°C) for ten days. Finally, move to a cool storage space.

Kvass – a lactic acid-fermented beverage

(for a one quart/liter preserving jar)

2	cups fruit (apples, pears)	3/4	cup real sourdough
4	tbsp sauerkraut juice,		bread
	or 2 tbsp fresh sauerkraut		peppermint and/
	water for filling up the pot		or lemon balm

Put sourdough bread in warm water to dissolve it. (Remember to buy sourdough bread that is made without preservatives.) Wash and grate the fruit. Mix bread, fruit, lactic acid-fermented sauerkraut juice, and herbs in the pot, then fill the jar with water. Leave the jar at room temperature for two to three days, then put in a cold place. Strain the contents before serving.

You can enjoy this drink right after fermentation is finished, but it will improve with longer storage. Although most of the bacteria in kvass are the lactic acid-producing species, there are also some that will produce alcohol. You may dilute this drink if you wish. After two to three months, transfer the contents into bottles, filling them to the brim.

Beet Kvass

Use beets in place of some of the fruit—you will get a juice with a beautiful red color.

Kvass With Honey

Try adding honey to all the kvass recipes according to taste—a few tablespoons of dissolved honey produce a very delicate aroma.

Has the Fermentation Been Successful?

Having faithfully followed the instructions in your first attempt at lactic acid fermentation, you might well ask, "How do I know whether the fermentation went according to plan?"

Our answer would be that the aroma and taste of your product will tell you. A successful fermentation develops a characteristic, pleasing aroma. The taste should be pleasant and slightly sour. If you do not want to rely on your tongue alone, buy some litmus paper at your local drugstore and test the pH-value.

We should briefly explain that pH-value is a measure of the degree of acidity or alkalinity of a fluid, and is rated on a scale of one to fourteen. The lower the pH number, the more acidic the fluid. Around the middle, at pH 7, the solution is neutral. Above pH 7, the solution is alkaline. For lactic acid fermentation, the critical point is at 4.1 pH. Below this value, decay cannot occur. Decomposition or decay has its own characteristic and unpleasant smell; when this happens, butyric acid forms, and the vegetables turn slimy. Throw them away and try again!

Vegetables grown too rapidly, or those over-fertilized or sprayed with pesticides can spoil during fermentation. These are the most common causes of failed fermentation. Fermentation can also fail if insufficient salt is added.

Under certain conditions, too much yeast will form. Yeast fungus contributes to the flavor and aroma and should be present to some extent in lactic acid-fermented preserves. If, however, it multiplies too fast, and "takes over," the lactic acid-fermented bacteria will be destroyed. Excessive yeast production can be recognized by gas bubbles rising in the vegetables. The simplest way to remedy this problem is to chill the pot.

You could also boil part of the fluid and add more salt. Be careful, though—the shelf-life of vegetables with excessive yeast production is limited and they should be eaten without too much delay.

As you may have gathered from this book, all kinds of variations and combinations of preserves are possible using lactic acid fermentation. The main reason that lactic acid fermentation is such an exciting and flexible technique is that it is an organic process, carried out by living creatures.

*Food probably has a very great influence on the condition of men.
Wine exercises a more visible influence, food does it more slowly
but perhaps just as surely. Who knows if a well-prepared soup was
not responsible for the pneumatic pump or a poor one for a war?*

G. C. Lichtenberg (1742–99)

Part III

Healing With
Lactic Acid Fermentation

Medicine from the Kitchen

Healing Secrets in the Pot

Hippocrates, the founding father of medicine, demanded that our nourishment be curative, and that our cures be nourishing. Over the millennia his words have lost none of their urgency and significance.

Lactic acid-fermented vegetables supremely fulfill Hippocrates's ideal of nutritious and curative nourishment. They are not only tasty, but they also exert stimulating and healing effects on our various body functions.

Modern research has confirmed what people have known from experience: lactic acid bacteria create an environment in the intestines in which bacteria that are sensitive to acidity, such as those causing cholera and typhoid, just cannot develop. This symbiosis between man and his intestinal bacteria balances our various life processes. Sauerkraut eliminates disease-causing "bad" bacteria and reintroduces friendly "good" bacteria (such as *Lactobacillus acidophilus*). Such friendly bacteria, which are often destroyed by antibiotic residues in our food, are necessary for healthy digestion and proper elimination of waste products.

In the process of fermentation, the carbohydrates in the vegetables break down and form lactic acid, which activates the gastric juices and thus helps to break down the ingested food for correct assimilation. Since lactic acid is a strong acid, it can in part replace the hydrochloric acid present in the stomach. This is of particular benefit to the elderly and those who otherwise experience a weakness of hydrochloric acid and other enzyme production. With age, the digestive organs weaken. While raw foods are often not well tolerated by the elderly, lactic acid-fermented vegetables are already "predigested" by the fermentation process and are, therefore, easily digestible.

Lactic acid-fermented foods are well-tolerated by people who have problems digesting lactose. In the human intestines, lactose is split into its components of glucose and galactose through the action of the enzyme lactase, and thereafter easily enters the bloodstream. Additionally, small quantities of lactose reach the lower intestines and are converted into lactic acid by the intestinal flora. For this reason, lactose has a positive effect on the intestinal flora and the general condition of the lower bowels. The toning action of lactose is important for rebuilding the intestinal flora following antibiotic treatment, or in the case of chronic constipation.

Some people's lactose intolerance is caused by a deficiency in the enzyme lactase. Lactose intolerance can also be the result of a digestive tract disease. Older people can become somewhat more lactose intolerant than they were in their younger years, when there were still sufficient amounts of lactase generated in their systems.

When lactose is incompletely digested, larger than normal amounts reach the lower bowels where they are fermented by intestinal bacteria. This can give rise to bloating, diarrhea and bellyaches. Fortunately, lactose intolerant people can still enjoy lactic acid-fermented foods like sauerkraut because fermented lactose is more easily digested by the lower bowels than regular lactose.

Lactic acid-fermented vegetables—and sauerkraut in particular—are highly nutritious and low in calories. They also contain high amounts of vitamins and minerals. A half-cup portion of sauerkraut contains the following nutrients:

- 20 calories (kcal)
- 1.1 g protein
- 0.2 g fat
- 3.4 g carbohydrate
- 1.4 g raw fiber
- traces of vitamin A
- 20 mcg vitamin B_1
- 200 mcg vitamin B_2
- 18 mg vitamin C
- 730 mg sodium
- 490 mg potassium
- 31 mg phosphorus
- 46 mg calcium
- 0.5 mg iron

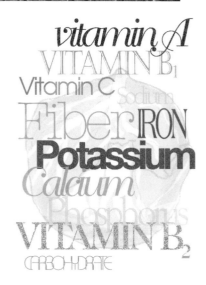

Lactic acid-fermented vegetables activate the pancreas causing the level of sugar in the blood and the urine to lessen (good news for people with diabetes!). Since the vegetables (with the exception of green beans) are not heated during the fermentation process, their enzymes, which are susceptible to chemicals as well as to heat, are preserved. Enzymes play a crucial role in our metabolism; without them, metabolic activity would be extraordinarily slow.

Sauerkraut (and lactic acid-fermented vegetables in general) also causes a lowering of blood pressure. This hypotensive effect is based on sauerkraut's choline content. Choline is a substance that balances and regulates the composition of the blood. On top of that, choline also lowers the level of fats in the blood. And finally, it is a superb natural remedy for constipation.

And there is yet another vital substance present in sauerkraut: acetylcholine, a compound released at many autonomic nerve endings, and believed to have a specific function in the transmission of nerve impulses. Acetylcholine has a pronounced calming effect on the nervous system and, as mentioned earlier, stimulates the peristaltic movement of the intestines. It also improves sleep patterns, lowers blood pressure and strengthens the heart. However, acetylcholine is susceptible to heat. This means that in order to get the full benefit of its therapeutic effect, sauerkraut should not be cooked.

Lactic acid fermentation is a good method of preserving vegetables, and eating vegetables preserved in this way is an effective way to attain health and maintain it. Our body certainly does not need huge amounts of lactic acid-fermented vegetables—we don't have to eat sauerkraut until we are overfull! Small amounts, taken regularly, are quite sufficient to initiate many healing processes.

Keeping Cancer in Check

Lactic acid-fermented vegetables are firmly established as healing agents in holistic cancer therapies. In his book *Internal Cancer Therapy and the Nutrition of the Cancer Patient*, Dr. Werner Zabel draws attention to the fact that the presence of a cancerous growth is always accompanied by a lack of hydrochloric acid and of enzymes. Regular consumption of lactic acid-fermented foods, especially sauerkraut, provides the body with the necessary hydrochloric acid and enzymes. If our food is poorly digested and decomposed, our intestines become overloaded with metabolic toxins that must then be processed by the liver.

Most modern guides to natural healing methods recommend regular intake of lactic acid as co-therapy for cancer. Many cancer researchers, among them Kuhl, Scheller, Kleine, Herberger and Zabel, advocate holistic approaches to cancer that focus on food sources such as lactic acid fermentation. Today it is well known that cancer is rampant in highly civilized countries where food intake is highly synthetic (canned, manufactured, frozen, etc.), and rare or absent in countries where diets consist mainly of fresh or home-preserved foods, including products made by lactic acid fermentation.

It is clear, then, that in cancer cases, food consumption should consist of more lactic acid-fermented foods (vegeta-

bles and milk products)
because the lactic acid helps
the intestinal flora that is
often impaired by cancers.
Lactic acid helps to pro-
duce B-vitamins via the
intestinal flora. It also
stimulates cell metabo-
lism, which is severely
impaired by cancer. Lactic
acid is also a detoxifier. Lactic
acid-fermented vegetables, provided they are made with high-
quality raw materials (i.e., organic
cabbage, raw certified milk, etc.), are effective in helping
normalize cell respiration, metabolism and the crucial acid-
alkaline or pH-balance of the body.

According to Kleine, and following the research of
O. Th. Weiss, patients with intestinal cancer should avoid
fermented milk products and instead use lactic acid-fermented vegetable products, as the vegetable-derived lactic
acid fermentation is more effective with this particular type
of cancer. The special medicinal importance of lactic acid-
fermented vegetables and their juices, and in particular
sauerkraut, is thoroughly investigated and addressed in various books by Dr. Johannes Kuhl, including *Checkmate to
Cancer*.

Kuhl, a scientific advisor to the European Atomic
Energy Commission in Rome, states that "lactic acid is the
functional element of growth in nature and the regenerative
component for damaged plant and animal cells. The lactic
acid-containing products, like no other nutrients, have an
exclusive, protective and healing effect on chronic diseases,
of which cancer is one." The importance of these products in
preventing chronic disorders and cancer can be demonstrat-
ed in the low incidence of these diseases in countries where
lactic acid-fermented foods are a staple. These countries

include Russia, China, Bulgaria and Romania.

An example of the powerful healing effect of lactic acid-fermented products can be seen in the treatment of polyps, often associated with cancerous growths. After four to six weeks of intensive ingestion of lactic acid-fermented vegetables, polyps will disappear. A recurrence of the polyps will be unlikely if these fermented vegetables continue to be a staple in the regular diet. Kuhl has observed this treatment first hand, and recommends that anyone suffering from polyps should try it. He feels very strongly that every effort should be made to make lactic acid-fermented products a dietary staple. Kuhl believes that if this were the case, the incidences of cancer would decrease substantially.

Kuhl also advocates lactic acid consumption and treatments as a remedy for radiation sickness. He states that diseased cells are more sensitive to ionizing radiation damage than healthy tissues. Kuhl's advice offers new hope for cancer patients who have undergone radiation therapy and are looking for ways of reversing radiation damage. It could also help patients who for various reasons have had extensive x-rays or x-ray therapy. Kuhl warns against treating cancer patients with radiation therapy, and opposes the irradiation of foodstuffs for the purpose of preservation.

Kuhl's views on healing cancerous growths using lactic acid are supported by other researchers. The remarkable rarity of cancer in Egypt is mentioned by K. H. Bauer in his book *The Cancer Problem*. Bauer notes that in Egypt, lactic acid fermentation is widely practiced with almost all kinds of vegetables. He also found that Arabs drink substantial amounts of sour milk. And, of course, lactic acid-fermented yogurt, kefir and sourdough breads are also consumed in great quantity. For all these reasons, Kuhl strongly advises eating lactic acid-fermented foods.

Superior and Inferior Lactic Acids
Lactic acid fermentation gives rise to two different forms of lactic acid: L(+) and D(-) lactic acid. Lactic acid-fermented

foods like sauerkraut contain more of the L(+) acid which, happily, is the physiologically superior form because it corresponds to the human metabolism.

First and foremost, L(+) lactic acid is necessary for the creation of energy in the muscles, liver and red blood cells. It becomes one of the base substances for making glucose, fatty acids and hormones—things the body needs continuously for health and survival. And, while the body can make its own lactic acid, supplementing our diets with foods rich in L(+) lactic acid has many positive effects on our metabolism.

The latest scientific research suggests that D(-) lactic acid, under conditions of normal ingestion, does not present a burden to the human metabolism. Nevertheless, many authorities state that tumor cells and disturbed intestinal flora produce mainly D(-) lactic acid. The appearance of D(-) lactic acid inside the human metabolism must therefore be considered a sign of metabolic disturbance.

D(-) lactic acid build-up is often blamed for muscle aches and cramps. While there is a correlation between them, it must be made clear that D(-) lactic acid in the muscles is usually produced during hard aerobic activity when there is insufficient oxygen coming from the blood to the muscles. Oxygen is necessary to metabolize pyruvic acid (a "good acid") and, in extreme aerobic conditions, the available oxygen is insufficient to meet the needs of the contracting muscles. The result is that pyruvic acid is converted to

D(-) lactic acid. When this happens the muscles begin to ache or even cramp due to the build-up of lactic acid in the muscle fibers. Not to worry, however, with enough rest and intake of carbohydrate-rich foods (such as—you guessed it—sauerkraut) the cramps or tightness will soon go away.

Medical evidence assures us that L(+) lactic acid is preferred as a food source. Happily, lactic acid-fermented sauerkraut contains mainly this type of acid.

The Healing Cabbage

With the advent of new diseases and new methods of treating them, the healing power of cabbage was often overlooked. Today, however, the healing benefits of cabbage are being rediscovered. Various skin diseases respond well to cabbage poultices (mashed leaves or sauerkraut). Intestinal diseases have been successfully treated with cabbage, as have fever and rheumatic pains. Tumors have been reduced with cabbage applications from within and without. The beautiful thing about treatment with cabbage is that it is totally natural and without any side-effects.

According to herbalist and botanist Camille Droz, a poultice of cabbage leaves augments the secretions of

A cabbage leaf poultice augments the secretions of festering wounds and speeds up the natural healing process.

festering wounds and inflamed skin tissues, and penetrates healthy skin to heal diseased tissue underneath.

Droz also recommends an application of cabbage leaves in cases of gangrene and a great number of skin conditions. In his writings he provides numerous proofs for his claims and has published many letters from healed and happy patients. It is remarkable that lactic acid-fermented cabbage as well as raw, crushed or mashed cabbage, offers such great healing powers.

Professor Hartmann, a famous German medical doctor, recommends raw sauerkraut for the cleansing of septic wounds. This seemingly strange recommendation is reinforced by the well-known German surgeon Professor F. Sauerbruch, who confirmed that surgical wounds healed much quicker and better if patients ate raw sauerkraut during recovery. The healing action of the lactic acid in the sauerkraut is not surprising given that lactic acid alleviates ailments like hardening of the arteries, rheumatism, gout and liver problems.

Sauerkraut is also recommended by medical authorities for blood cleansing and general debility. And medical doctors have successfully treated asthma, chronic constipation and sciatica with a therapy of several weeks of regular sauerkraut eating. The healing effect of sauerkraut is primarily due to the presence of lactic acid and choline.

Raw sauerkraut juice is an excellent and natural remedy for worms, especially in children suffering from roundworm. It is inexpensive, and healthier than using prescription drugs. It seems that sauerkraut even has bactericidal properties, in particular, against typhoid bacteria, as evidenced by a typhoid fever epidemic in Stuttgart, Germany during 1952–53. Sauerkraut was systematically tested as a possible cause of the epidemic, but it was found that, contrary to being causative, it killed the offending bacteria within six hours, provided the sauerkraut was fresh.

In a well-known text on home remedies, Dr. Bernd Jurgens advocates the use of lactic acid-fermented sauerkraut in both health and sickness.

He offers the following sound advice on the use of sauerkraut. (Unless otherwise indicated, the sauerkraut is to be eaten in small amounts throughout the day for a therapeutic term of six weeks, and repeated throughout the year, as may be necessary.)

Anemia
Daily, one lb (1/2 kg) of lactic acid-fermented sauerkraut eaten in small amounts throughout the day.

Arteriosclerosis
Daily, one lb (1/2 kg) of lactic acid-fermented sauerkraut eaten in small amounts throughout the day and repeated several times a year.

Bronchial asthma
Daily, one lb (1/2 kg) of raw lactic acid-fermented sauerkraut mixed with one raw onion and one raw garlic clove.

Diabetes
Three times daily, 1/2 glass of sauerkraut juice taken 1 1/2 hours before meals, plus, daily, one lb (1/2 kg) of lactic acid-fermented sauerkraut eaten in small amounts throughout the day.

Gout
Daily, one lb (1/2 kg) of lactic acid-fermented sauerkraut eaten in small amounts throughout the day.

Longevity
Daily, one lb (1/2 kg) of lactic acid-fermented sauerkraut eaten in small amounts throughout the day for four weeks at least twice a year.

Rheumatism
Daily, one lb (1/2 kg) of lactic acid-fermented sauerkraut eaten in small amounts throughout the day.

Worms (roundworm, tapeworm, pinworm, etc.)

Drink 1/2 glass of sauerkraut juice before each meal and eat 1/2 cup sauerkraut on an empty stomach each morning until the worms are gone for good.

Conclusion

Whether you incorporate sauerkraut into your diet for preventative or curative reasons—or even if you do it simply because it tastes great, you can do so with the certainty that many body processes and organs will be stimulated and strengthened by the workings of the lactic acid.

The Cultured Cabbage is an introduction to this ancient and remarkable food, one that has sustained emperors, explorers and common people for thousands of years. Lactic acid-fermented vegetables prove that we can be well fed and well nourished at once—a rare combination in this age of processed and synthetic foods. Once you have tried the recipes in this book your imagination will leap to the fun task of creating more delicious and healthful dishes of your own. *Guten Appetit!*

Notes

1. Translated from the German by Klaus Kaufmann: "Es ist ein großer Schatz von Segensgaben im Kraut versteckt und im Gestein vergraben. Süße, heilige Natur, Laß mich gehn auf deiner Spur."
2. Translated from the German by Klaus Kaufmann: "Ein Viertel dessen, was die Menschen essen, für den Körper reicht. Der Rest macht die Menschen krank, die Geldbeutel schlank und die Ärzte reich."
3. Translated from the German by Klaus Kaufmann: "In der Überzeugung, daß das Sauerkraut durch seine Säure der Fäulnis kräftig widerstehen müsse, aß Cook täglich selbst und bewog seine Offiziere, das gleiche zu tun." Georg Forster is the son of the German naturalist Reinhold Forster, who with his son, accompanied Cook on his second voyage.
4. See *Kefir Rediscovered!* by Klaus Kaufmann.
5. See *kombucha Rediscovered!* by Klaus Kaufmann.
6. Translated from the German by Klaus Kaufmann: "Wo du durch Nahrungsmittel heilen kannst, da verordne keine Arzneien, und wo einfache Mittel ausreichen, da nimm keine zusammengesetzten."

Bibliography

Bauer, K. H. *The Cancer Problem.*

Bittere Pillen Autorenteam. *Kursbuch Gesundheits-Fahrplan für ein gesundes Leben.* Germany.

Bruker, Dr. M.O. *Gesund durch richtiges Essen.* Germany: Tomus Verlag.

Droz, Camille. *Von den Wunderbaren Heilwirkungen des Kohlblattes.* Les Geneveys-Sur-Coffrane, Neuenburg, Switzerland, 1985.

Eichholtz, Dr. Fritz. *Die biologische Milchsäure und ihre Entstehung in vegetabilischem Material.* Eden, Germany, 1975.

Jürgens, Dr. Bernd. *Hausrezepte der Naturheilkunde—Eine Sammlung homöopatischer und biologischer Heilmethoden.* Bern and Stuttgart: Hallwag Verlag, 1982.

Kaufmann, Klaus. *Kefir Rediscovered!* Burnaby, BC: *alive* books, 1997.

Kaufmann, Klaus. *kombucha Rediscovered!* Burnaby, BC: *alive* books, 1996.

Kuhl, Dr. Johannes. *Biologischer Strahlenschutz: Das milchsaure Getreideschrot—Müsli.* Bern, Switzerland Humata Verlag.

Kuhl, Dr. Johannes. *Krebs und Bestrahlung: Ein Irrtum Moderner Medizin.* Braunlage, Germany: Viadrina Verlag, 1966.

Leibold, Gerhard. *Das große Hausbuch der Natur Heilkunde.* Bassermann, Germany.

Leitzmann, Dr. Claus, and Helmut Million. *Vollwertküche für Genießer: Mit Lust und Liebe.* Germany: Falken Verlag, 1991.

Locher, Hans-Rudolf, and H. L. Friedrich. *Lehm/Moor/Kohlblatt.* Zürich, Switzerland: Verlag Volks-gesundheit.

Luh, Bor Shiun and Jasper Guy Woodroof. *Commercial Vegetable Processing.* 2nd ed. New York: Avi Book.

Prescott, S.C., C.G. Dunn and Cecil Gordon. *Prescott and Dunn's Industrial Microbiology.* Westport, CT: Avi Pub., 1982.

Schneider, Dr. E. *Nutze die Heilkraft unserer Nahrung.* Hamburg, Germany: Saatkorn-Verlag, 1985.

Schöneck, Annelies. *Making Sauerkraut and Pickled Vegetables at Home.* Burnaby, BC: *alive* books, 1988.

Stanbury, P. F. and A. Whitaker. *Principles of Fermentation Technology.* Oxford, England: Pergamon Press, 1987.

Stirnimann, Beat. *Sauerkraut als Delikatesse Entdeckt.* Aarau, Switzerland: AT Verlag, 1988.

Taber, Clarence Wilbur. *Taber's Cyclopedic Medical Dictionary.* 17th ed. Philadelphia: F.A. Davis Co., 1989.

Trenev, Natasha, and Leon Chaitow, ND. *Probiotics: The Revolutionary Friendly Bacteria Way to Vital Health and Well-Being.* Wellingborough, England: Thorsons Publishing Group, 1990.

Trum Hunter, Beatrice. *Fermented Foods and Beverages: An Old Tradition.* New Canaan, CT: Keats, 1973.

Vonarburg, Bruno. *Gottes Segen in der Natur.* Stein am Rhein, Germany: Christiana-Verlag, 1977.

Weber, Marlis, and Isabel Wilden. *Lexikon der Gesunden Ernährung.* Germany: Hädecke Gesundheit, 1991.

Whitaker, John R. *Food Related Enzymes.* Washington, DC: American Chemical Society, 1974.

Index

Recommended Reading

Balch, Phyllis A. and James Balch. *Prescription for Dietary Wellness.* Greenfield, IN: PAB Publishing, Inc., 1992.

Chelf, Vicki Rae. *Arrowhead Mills Cookbook.* New York: Avery Publishing Group Inc., 1993.

Hupping, Carol. *Stocking Up.* New York: Fireside, 1986.

Jensen, Bernard. *Foods That Heal.* New York: Avery Publishing Group Inc., 1993.

Katzen, Mollie. *Enchanted Broccoli Forest.* Berkeley, CA: Ten Speed Press, 1995.

Kinard, Malvina. *Well Preserved.* New Canaan, CT: Keats Publishing Inc., 1994.

Moosewood Collective, The. *Sundays at Moosewood Restaurant.* Berkeley, CA: Ten Speed Press, 1994.

Moosewood Collective, The. *New Recipes From Moosewood Restaurant.* Berkeley, CA: Ten Speed Press, 1997.

Murray, Michael T. *Stomach Ailments and Digestive Disturbances: Getting Well Naturally.* Rocklin, CA: Prima Publishing, 1997.

Robertson, Laurel, Carol Flanders and Brian Ruppenthal. *Laurel's Kitchen Recipes.* Berkeley, CA: Ten Speed Press, 1993.

Webster, David. *Achieve Maximum Health.* Cardiff, CA: Hygeia Publishing, 1995.

Useful Addresses

alive Academy of Nutrition
7436 Fraser Park Drive
Burnaby, BC V5J 5B9
Tel: (604) 435-1919
Fax: (604) 435-4888

Nutri-Books US
790 West Tennessee Avenue
Denver, CO 80223
Tel: (303) 778-8383
Fax: (303) 744-9383
Contact: Mike van Meter

The fermentation crock with the airlock feature mentioned in this book is manufactured by:

Harsch Steinzeugwerk
Steinzeugwerk Harsch
Gmbh+Co. KG
Postfach 12 80-7518 bretten
Tel: (0 72 52) 77-0
Telex: 78 531 harod
Fax: (0 72 52) 8 67 74

The Harsch crocks are sold in health food stores and natural food stores across Canada and the United States. Please contact one of the distributors listed below:

Flora Distributors Ltd.— Eastern Canada
396 Deerhurst Drive
Brampton, ON L6T 5H9
Tel: 1-800-387-7541
Fax: (905) 791-1773

Flora Distributors Ltd.— Western Canada
7400 Fraser Park Drive
Burnaby, BC V5J 5B9
Tel: 1-800-663-0617
Fax: (604) 436-6060

Flora Inc., US
805 Badger Road
Box 950
Lynden, WA 98264
Tel: 1-800-446-2110

About the Authors

Klaus Kaufmann is an internationally recognized scientific writer, holistic life science counselor, lecturer and Ecotrophologist at the *alive* Academy of Nutrition in Burnaby, BC. Kaufmann produced numerous bestsellers, in particular the noted *Silica—The Amazing Gel* (1993–97) and its companion volume *Silica—The Forgotten Nutrient* (1990–93). These works expound silicon's uses in healing and prevention and made Kaufmann the foremost authority on the nutrient uses of this mineral, resulting in a lifetime appointment to an international advisory board on sillica. His new German language edition *Silicum-Heilund durch Ursubstanz* sold out all 25,000 copies in 1997, its first year of publication. Translations into French and Japanese are now underway.

Kaufmann's other major works include *Devil's Claw Root* (1994) and *The Joy of Juice Fasting* (1990), a timely approach to health. *Eliminating Poison in Your Mouth* (1991) is a study on mercury amalgam. Kaufmann's popular *kombucha Rediscovered!* (1995) and *Kefir Rediscovered!* (1996) books entertainingly reveal ancient foods as home remedies and engaging hobbies, continued here.

Klaus and his family live below Simon Fraser University at Burnaby Mountain in British Columbia, where, in addition to his full researching and writing work (he is researching a major work on electromagnetic energies), Klaus is also studying for a Doctor of Science degree.

Annelies Schöneck was born in Germany in 1920. After completing a teaching degree in farming economy, she moved to Sweden in 1953. Since then, she has accumulated a vast knowledge of human nutrition, and has become a pioneer in the cultivation and refinement of natural lactic acid-fermented foods.

Through her related publications, seminars and workshops, Schöneck has reached a worldwide audience. Her books on the natural lactic acid fermentation of vegetables, including this revised edition of *Making Sauerkraut and Pickled Vegetables at Home*, have been translated into several languages.

Other books by Klaus Kaufmann published by *alive* **books:**

Kefir Rediscovered!

kombucha Rediscovered!

Silica—The Amazing Gel

Devil's Claw Root and Other Natural Remedies for Arthritis

by Rachel Carston (revised by Klaus Kaufmann)